Edition Schott

Paul Hindemith
1895 – 1963

9 Short Songs
for American School Songbooks

(1983)

for 1-4 voices with and without accompaniment (piano),
scored for solo voice or chorus

für 1-4 Singstimmen mit und ohne Begleitung (Klavier),
solistisch oder chorisch besetzt

Full Score / Partitur

Edited by / Herausgegeben von
Luitgard Schader

ED 20454
ISMN 979-0-001-15364-5

www.schott-music.com

Mainz · London · Berlin · Madrid · New York · Paris · Prague · Tokyo · Toronto
© 2010 SCHOTT MUSIC GmbH & Co. KG, Mainz · Printed in Germany

Preface

In the summer of 1937 Marshall Bartholomew visited Paul Hindemith in Berlin on behalf of the American publishers *Silver, Burdett & Company* to ask him to compose a few little songs for a series of school books. The publishers evidently doubted whether this distinctly modern German composer could really write music simple enough for children, for Bartholomew's report of his meeting with Hindemith offers reassurance: "He is without question the foremost German composer of his time and the only one who is internationally known and admired. And I have the feeling that in spite of his extreme modernism in his big compositions he will be successful in writing something which children can sing and will enjoy. His work for children that I have seen and heard up to date has been distinctly successful with the children themselves." He also pointed out that Hindemith had naturally chosen songs with English words for use in American schools.

The Spider's Web and *Romance* were written during a concert tour in February of the following year; Hindemith then sent both pieces to Bartholomew with the comment 'if you like these songs, you can have a few more of them. It would be nice to have a few texts to choose from.' These two pieces evidently met with the client's approval, for Hindemith sent seven more songs just a few days later.

As the pieces were intended for various age groups, Hindemith wrote music at varying levels of difficulty. Some of the songs are in one or two parts with piano accompaniment, others for four mixed voices a cappella. They were not originally published together, but included in various school song books – and two of the songs remained unpublished for several decades. The composer did not give a specific title to these pieces, referring to them as 'school songs' or 'American songs'; his personal record of compositions refers (in German) to 'Nine little songs for an American school songbook'.

When these nine songs were published together for the first time in the complete Hindemith edition in 2009 it was decided that the work should have an American title, for the composer wanted his compositions to be identified with the language of the country for which the pieces had been written. Hindemith's collection of songs is published here for the first time in a separate edition under the title *Nine Short Songs for American School Songbooks*.

Luitgard Schader
Translation Julia Rushworth

Vorwort

Im Sommer 1937 besuchte Marshall Bartholomew im Auftrag des amerikanischen Verlags *Silver, Burdett & Company* Paul Hindemith in Berlin, um ihn um die Komposition von einigen kleinen Liedern zu bitten, die in einer Schulbuchreihe erscheinen sollten. Offensichtlich war die Verlagsleitung etwas unsicher, ob dieser sehr moderne deutsche Komponist wirklich auch leicht genug für Kinder schreiben könne, denn Bartholomew berichtete beinahe beruhigend von seiner Begegnung mit Hindemith. „Er ist ohne Frage der bedeutendste deutsche Komponist seiner Zeit und der einzige, der international bekannt ist und bewundert wird. Und ich habe das Gefühl, dass er trotz der extrem modernen Musiksprache, die er in seinen großen Kompositionen benutzt, auch sehr erfolgreich Stücke schreiben wird, die Kinder singen können und die ihnen auch Freude machen. Seine Kompositionen für Kinder, die ich bis jetzt gesehen oder gehört habe, sind bei den Kindern selbst ausgesprochen beliebt." Als Besonderheit hob er außerdem hervor, dass Hindemith für amerikanische Schüler selbstverständlich Liedtexte in englischer Sprache ausgesucht habe.

Erst im Februar des kommenden Jahres entstanden während einer Konzerttournee *The Spider's Web* und *Romance* und Hindemith sandte die beiden Stücke an Bartholomew mit der Bemerkung, „wenn Ihnen diese Lieder recht sind, können Sie noch einige davon haben. Dann hätte ich noch um einige Texte zur Auswahl gebeten". Offensichtlich entsprachen die beiden Stücke voll und ganz den Erwartungen des Auftraggebers, denn Hindemith ließ ihnen innerhalb weniger Tage 7 weitere Lieder folgen.

Da die Stücke für unterschiedliche Altersgruppen gedacht waren, schrieb Hindemith in verschiedenen Schwierigkeitsgraden. Einige der Lieder sind ein- oder zweistimmig mit Klavierbegleitung gesetzt, andere für vier gemischte Stimmen a cappella. Sie erschienen deshalb auch nicht gleichzeitig, sondern wurden als Einzelstücke in unterschiedliche Schulbücher eingereiht, zwei von ihnen blieben sogar über viele Jahrzehnte hinweg unveröffentlicht. Deshalb hatte der Komponist selbst auch keinen Werktitel festgelegt, sondern immer nur von „den Schulliedern" oder den „amerikanischen Liedern" gesprochen, in sein privates Werkverzeichnis notierte er *9 kleine Lieder für ein amerikanisches Schulliederbuch*.

Als die 9 Lieder 2009 in der Hindemith-Gesamtausgabe erstmals gemeinsam publiziert wurden, entschloss man sich, das Werk mit einem amerikanischen Titel zu versehen, denn der Komponist wollte, dass seine Kompositionen immer in der Sprache des Landes bezeichnet werden, für das die Stücke geschrieben wurden. So entstand der Titel *9 Short Songs for American School Songbooks*, unter dem Hindemiths Liedsammlung hier erstmals in einer Einzelausgabe veröffentlicht wird.

Luitgard Schader

Contents / Inhalt

1. The Spider's Web

(Charlotte Druitt Cole)

Paul Hindemith
(1938)

53 000

2. Romance

(E. F. A. Geach)

Paul Hindemith
(1938)

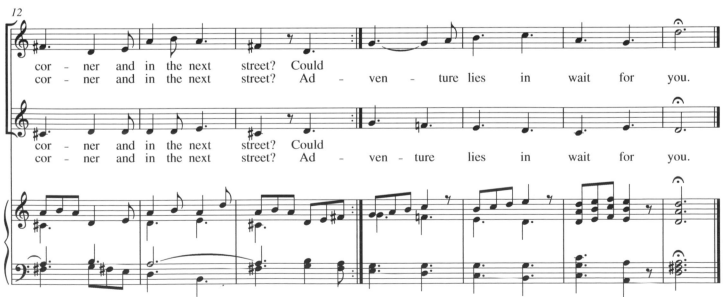

53 000

3. Rain

(Annie Willis McCullough)

Paul Hindemith
(1938)

The spring rain helps the bush-es bud a - long the gar-den path; the sum-mer rain gives dust-y leaves a most re-fresh - ing bath; the fall rain pelts the chest-nuts down up - on the ground be - low; the win-ter rain ___ ah, I for - get! The win - ter rain is snow.

53 000

4. Prayer for a Pilot

(Cecil Roberts)

Paul Hindemith
(1938)

5. April Rain

(Robert Loveman)

Paul Hindemith
(1938)

6. Thrush Song

(Clinton Scollard)

Paul Hindemith
(1938)

53 000

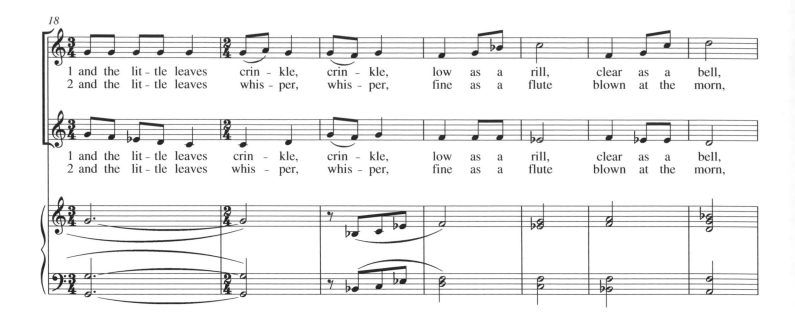

7. A Rain Song

(Clinton Scollard)

Paul Hindemith
(1938)

53 000

8. The Sea Gypsy

(Richard Hovey)

Paul Hindemith
(1938)

9. Young and Old

(Charles Kingsley)

Paul Hindemith
(1938)

53 000

Schott Music, Mainz 53 000

Song texts / Liedtexte

1 The Spider's Web

Spider! Spider! What are you spinning?
A cloak for a fairy I'm just beginning.
What is it made of? Tell me true.
Threads of moonshine and pearls of dew.
When will the fairy be wearing it?
Tonight, when the glowworm lamps are lit.
Can I see her if I come peeping?
All good children must be then sleeping.

(Charlotte Druitt Cole; c. 1900)

2 Romance

Round the next corner and in the next street
adventure lies in wait for you.
Oh, who can tell what you may meet
round the next corner and in the next street?
Could life be anything but sweet
when all is hazardous and new
round the next corner and in the next street?
Adventure lies in wait for you.

(E. F. A. Geach; c. 1900)

3 Rain

The spring rain helps the bushes bud
along the garden path;
the summer rain gives dusty leaves
a most refreshing bath;
the fall rain pelts the chestnuts down
upon the ground below;
the winter rain – ah, I forget!
The winter rain is snow.

(Annie Willis McCullough; c. 1900)

4 Prayer for a Pilot

Lord of Sea and Earth and Air,
listen to the Pilot's prayer –
Send him wind that's steady and strong,
grant that his engine sings the song
of flawless tone, by which he knows
it shall not fail him where he goes;
gliding, landing, in curve, half-roll –
Grant him, o Lord, a full control,
that he may learn in heights of Heaven
the rapture altitude has given,
that he shall know the joy they feel
who ride Thy realms on Birds of Steel.

(Cecil Roberts; 1892-1976)

5 April Rain

It is not raining rain for me,
it's raining daffodils;
in every dimpled drop I see
wild flowers on the hills.
The clouds of gray engulf the day
and overwhelm the town;
it is not raining rain to me,
it's raining roses down.

It is not raining rain to me,
but fields of clover bloom,
where any buccaneering bee
can find a bed and room.
A health, a health unto the happy,
a fig for him who frets!
It is not raining rain to me,
it's raining violets.

(Robert Loveman; 1864-1923)

6 Thrush Song

Hark to the song of the thrush,
at the fall of the dusk and dew;
piercing the twilight hush,
thrilling it through and through.
While the first stars twinkle, twinkle,
and the little leaves crinkle, crinkle,
low as a rill, clear as a bell,
down from the hill, up from the dell,
and all for me and you!

List to the song of the thrush,
from the shadows cool and deep,
from the heart of the underbrush
where the pixy people creep.
While the winds grow crisper, crisper,
and the little leaves whisper, whisper,
fine as a flute blown at the morn,
soft as a lute, or fairy horn,
a call to the land of sleep!

(Clinton Scollard; 1860-1932)

7 A Rain Song

Don't you love to lie and listen,
listen to the rain,
with its little patter, patter,
and its tiny clatter, clatter,
and its silvery spatter, spatter,
on the roof and on the pane?

Yes, I love to lie and listen,
listen to the rain.
It's the fairies – Pert and Plucky,
Nip and Nimbletoes and Lucky,
Trip and Thimblenose and Tucky,
on the roof and on the pane.

That's my dream the while I listen,
listen to the rain.
I can see them running races,
I can watch their laughing faces
At their gleeful games and graces,
on the roof and on the pane!

(Clinton Scollard; 1860-1932)

8 The Sea Gypsy

I am fevered with the sunset,
I am fretful with the bay,
for the wanderthirst is on me
and my soul is in Cathay.

There's a schooner in the offing,
with her topsails shot with fire,
and my heart has gone aboard her
for the Islands of Desire.

I must forth again tomorrow!
With the sunset I must be
hull down on the trail of rapture
in the wonder of the Sea.

(Richard Hovey; 1864-1900)

9 Young and Old

When all the world is young, lad,
and all the trees are green;
and every goose a swan, lad,
and every lass a queen;
then hey for boot and horse, lad,
and round the world away;
young blood must have its course, lad,
and every dog his day.

When all the world is old, lad,
and all the trees are brown;
and all the sport is stale, lad,
and all the wheels run down;
creep home, and take your place there,
the spent and maimed among;
God grant you find one face there,
you loved when all was young.

(Charles Kingsley; 1819-1875)